Contents

Step 1: Three- and four-digit × one-digit

In **Multiplication 1** you learnt how to multiply by one-digit numbers, such as 847×7. In this book you will learn how to do **long multiplication**, where you multiply by two-, three- or four-digit numbers. First we will revise one-digit multiplication.

What to do (a reminder)

$847 \times 7 = ?$

1 Multiply the digits of the top number, working from right to left. If you get more than 9 in any multiplication, carry sets of ten over to the column to the left. $7 \times 7 = 49$ so write 9 in the units column and carry the 4 tens over. Write the carried tens below the line.

TTh	Th	H	T	U
		8	4	7
×				7
				9
			4	

2 Then multiply the tens digit, adding any carried tens. 4 tens × 7 = 28 tens, 28 tens + 4 carried tens = 32 tens. Write 2 in the tens column and carry the 3 hundreds.

		8	4	7
×				7
			2	9
		3	4	

3 Then multiply the hundreds digit, adding the carried hundreds. 8 hundreds × 7 = 56 hundreds. 56 hundreds + 3 carried hundreds = 59 hundreds. Write 9 in the hundreds column and carry the 5 thousands.

		8	4	7
×				7
	5	9	2	9
	5	3	4	

4 As the top number has no thousands you have no more multiplying to do, but you must write any carried thousands digits above the line to complete your answer.

Now you try

1

	9	1	4	8
×				5
			4	0
		2	4	

2

		3	9	6
×				8
				8
			4	

3

		7	6	1
×				6
			6	6
		3		

4

	2	9	8	7
×				4

Schofield & Sims

Written Calculation

Multiplication 2

Name _____

Introduction

This book helps you learn written multiplication. It explains each step. It gives you practice so your skills improve. The book also contains some tests. These help you check your progress.

How do I begin?

- Find a pencil, an eraser and some spare squared paper.

- Write your name on the cover of this book.

- Turn to Step 1 on page 4. Read the first few lines. They describe what you will learn.

- Then read **What to do**. Read slowly. Look at the example. Work through it carefully.

- Look at **Now you try** on page 4. Answer these questions. Use the example to help you. Write your workings and your answers in the grids.

- On page 5 are **More practice** and **Problem solving** questions. Answer all these questions too. Write your workin and your answers in the boxes and grids. Use spare paper if needed. In the **Problem solving** questions you use written multiplication to solve everyday problems.

- Look at the bottom of page 5. Tick to show if you found the step 'Easy', 'OK' or 'Difficult'. Be honest.

- Give your book to the adult who is helping you. The adult will mark your work. The adult will help you if necessary

Working through the book

- Work through all the steps in order. Do not miss out any steps. You will quickly learn to do written multiplication.

- Sometimes the answers or workings are already started to help you.

- There are three **Check-up tests** to help you revise the steps as you work through the book.

- The **Final test** at the end of the book will show you how much you have learnt.

Written Calculation: Multiplication 2 Answers (ISBN 978 07217 1275 8) provides answers to all the questions this book, including the tests.

The separate **Written Calculation: Teacher's Guide** (ISBN 978 07217 1278 9) contains full teaching notes and assessment resources. The **Teacher's Resource Book** (ISBN 978 07217 1300 7) contains photocopiable resources. Both cover the whole series and provide the teacher with valuable guidance and resources to support the teaching of written calculation. For free downloads and for further details on all the other **Written Calculation** books, visit **www.schofieldandsims.co.uk**

Published by Schofield & Sims Ltd, Dogley Mill, Fenay Bridge, Huddersfield HD8 0NQ, UK Tel 01484 607080 www.schofieldandsims.co.uk
First published in 2015. Copyright © Schofield & Sims Ltd, 2015.
Authors: **Hilary Koll and Steve Mills**
Hilary Koll and Steve Mills have asserted their moral rights under the Copyright, Designs and Patents Act, 1988, to be identified as the authors of this work.
British Library Cataloguing in Publication Data
A catalogue record for this book is available from the British Library.

Commissioned by **Carolyn Richardson Publishing Services (www.publiserve.co.uk)**
Design by **Ledgard Jepson Ltd**
Cover illustration by **Joe Hance (joehance.co.uk)**
Printed in the UK by **Wyndeham Gait Ltd, Grimsby, Lincolnshire**
ISBN 978 07217 1269 7

More practice   Set out these questions yourself to answer them.

5 6273 × 8 = ?

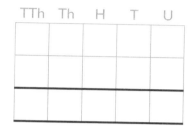

6 1924 × 7 = ?

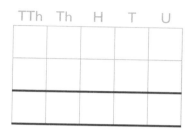

7 4178 × 5 = ?

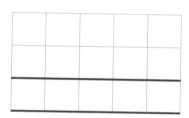

8 4557 × 9 = ?

Problem solving

9 Three people each win £1896 on the lottery. How much did they win altogether?

10 Every day 8925 people travel on a train. How many people travel on this train in a week?

11 Work out the missing digit in this multiplication.

	6	◯	8	4
×				8
5	4	2	7	2
	5	6	6	3

How did I find Step 1?   ☐ Easy   ☐ OK   ☐ Difficult

Step 2: Two-, three- and four-digit × 10 and × 20

TTh	Th	H	T	U
	3	4	7	9
×			1	0
3	4	7	9	0

Now you need to remind yourself how to multiply by 10 and 20. When multiplying by 10 the digits of the number being multiplied move one place to the left. We put a zero into the units column to complete the answer.

$3479 \times 20 = ?$

What to do	(a reminder)

1   To multiply by 20, first write zero in the units column.

TTh	Th	H	T	U
	3	4	7	9
×			2	0
			8	0
		1		

2   Then multiply the top number by 2, but writing the digits of the answer one place to the left. Start by multiplying the units digit by 2: $9 \times 2 = 18$. Write the 8 and carry 1 across.

3   Now multiply the tens digit and add the carried digit.

4   Then multiply the hundreds digit and add any carried digits.

5   Finally, multiply the thousands digit and add any carried digits.

TTh	Th	H	T	U
	3	4	7	9
×			2	0
6	9	5	8	0
	1	1		

Now you try

1

		3	1	8
	×		1	0
			8	0

2

		1	7	8	7
	×			2	0
				4	0
			1		

3

		4	8	3	6
	×			1	0
					0

4

			5	6	8	9
	×				2	0

More practice

5

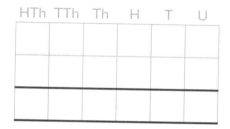

		7	7	7	7
×				2	0

6

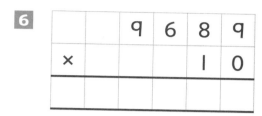

		9	6	8	9
×				1	0

et out these questions yourself to answer them.

7 4762 × 10 = ?

HTh	TTh	Th	H	T	U

8 9569 × 20 = ?

HTh	TTh	Th	H	T	U

Problem solving

How many times greater is the answer to 635 × 20 than the answer to 127 × 10?

A row of terraced houses is made from 20 joined houses, each identical in size. If the width of each house is 486cm, what is the width of the terrace?

Use the digits 6, 7, 8 and 9 in any order to make a four-digit number. Multiply the number by 20. Can you find the number that gives the answer 173940? Use spare paper for working.

How did I find Step 2?   ☐ Easy   ☐ OK   ☐ Difficult

Step 3: Two- and three-digit × a teens number
no carrying in the addition

Now you should be feeling confident enough to put it all together and multiply by a 'teens' number.

	H	T	
		2	0
×			1

What to do

$204 \times 13 = ?$

1 In the first row under the question multiply the top number by the **units** digit of the bottom number: 204×3. Remember to work from right to left and carry if necessary. It helps to make your carry numbers quite small if you can.

2 In the next row multiply the top number by 10. Simply write a zero in the units column first and multiply the top number by 1, writing the digits one place to the left. $204 \times 10 = 2040$

3 Finally add your two answers. Be careful **not** to add the carry marks you used when multiplying. Just add the digits of the two answers.
$612 + 2040 = 2652$

	Th	H	T	U	
			2	0	4
	×			1	3
			6	1₁	2	← 204×3
		2	0	4	0	← 204×10

		H	T	U	
		2	0	4
	×		1	3
		6	1₁	2	← 204×3
+	2	0	4	0	← 204×10
	2	6	5	2

Now you try

1

		1	3	2
×			1	4
		5₁	2	8	← 132×4
+				0	← 132×10

2

		1	3	1
×			1	5
		₁	5	5	← 131×5
+					← 131×10

3

		2	1	5
×			1	3
		4₁	5	← 215×3
+					← 215×10

4

		2	1	1
×			1	4
			4	← 211×4
+					← 211×10

More practice

5

		1	0	6
	×		1	6

← 106 × 6
← 106 × 10

6

		5	3	4
	×		1	4
	2₂	1₁	3₁	6
+				

← 534 × 4
← 534 × 10

7

		3	0	7
	×		1	3
+				

← 307 × 3
← 307 × 10

8

		2	3	4
	×		1	7
+				

← 234 × 7
← 234 × 10

et out these questions yourself to answer them.

9 43 × 15 = ?

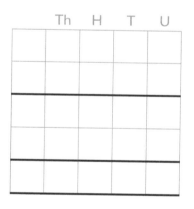

Th	H	T	U

10 214 × 13 = ?

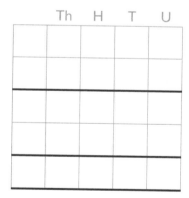

Th	H	T	U

Problem solving

11 Twelve people each win £214 on the lottery.
How much did they win altogether?

Step 4: Two- and three-digit × a teens number with carrying in the addition

These are similar to Step 3 but, when you add your two answers at the final stage, you might need to do some carrying.

	H	T	U
		2	5	1
×		1	3

$251 \times 13 = ?$

What to do

1. First multiply the top number by the units digit of the bottom number: 251×3. Remember to work from right to left and carry if necessary.

2. In the next row multiply the top number by 10. Simply write a zero in the units column first and multiply the top number by 1, writing the digits one place to the left. $251 \times 10 = 2510$

3. Finally add your two answers. Be careful not to add the carry marks you used when multiplying. Just add the digits of the two answers. You might need to carry when adding. Here 7 hundreds + 5 hundreds = 12 hundreds, so carry 1 thousand. $753 + 2510 = 3263$

Th	H	T	U	
		2	5	1	
×			1	3	
		7₁	5	3	← 251 × 3
	2	5	1	0	← 251 × 10

		2	5	1
	×		1	3
		7₁	5	3
+	2	5	1	0
	3	2	6	3

Now you try

1

			6	3
	×		1	3
				9	← 63 × 3
+				0	← 63 × 10

2

		1	8	4
	×		1	7
			₂8	← 184 × 7
+			0	← 184 × 10

3

		3	5	2
	×		1	5
		₁	0	← 352 × 5
+			0	← 352 × 10

4

		4	5	6
	×		1	4
			4	← 456 × 4
+				← 456 × 10

More practice

5

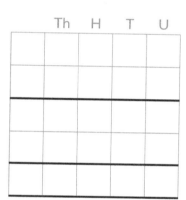

		1	9	6
	×		1	6

← 196 × 6

← 196 × 10

6

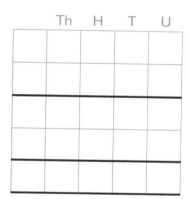

		3	6	4
	×		1	8

← 364 × 8

← 364 × 10

Set out these questions yourself to answer them.

7 44 × 19 = ?

Th	H	T	U

8 658 × 13 = ?

Th	H	T	U

Problem solving

Answer each of these multiplications using the same method.

111 × 19 = _____

222 × 19 = _____

333 × 19 = _____

Then look for patterns in the digits of the answers.
Can you use what you notice to predict the answer of 444 × 19? _____

How did I find Step 4?   Easy   OK    Difficult

Step 5: Three-digit × a teens number five-digit answers

Try these in the same way. Some of your answers may be five-digit numbers.

What to do

$986 \times 13 = ?$

1 First multiply the top number by the units digit of the bottom number. $986 \times 3 = 2958$

2 In the next row multiply the top number by 10. Remember to write a zero in the units column first. $986 \times 10 = 9860$

TTh	Th	H	T	U	
		9	8	6	
	×		1	3	
	2₂	9₂	5₁	8	← 986 × 3
	9	8	6	0	← 986 × 10

3 Finally add your two answers. Be careful not to add the carry marks you used when multiplying. Just add the digits of the two answers. You might need to carry when adding.

		9	8	6	
	×		1	3	
	2₂	9₂	5₁	8	
+		9	8	6	0
	1	2	8	1	8

Now you try

1

		9	7	3	
	×		1	5	
			₁	5	← 973 × 5
+				0	← 973 × 10

2

		5	7	6	
	×		1	9	
			₅	4	← 576 × 9
+				0	← 576 × 10

3

		8	6	9	
	×		1	4	
			₃	6	← 869 × 4
+					← 869 × 10

4

		9	5	8	
	×		1	8	
			₆	4	← 958 × 8
+					← 958 × 10

More practice

Each of these questions has two missing digits. Can you work out which are missing?

5

		7	○	4
	×		1	6
	4₄	4₂	0₂	4
+	7	○	4	0
1	1	7	4	4

6

		○	2	5
	×		1	7
	5₅	7₁	7₃	5
+	○	2	5	0
1	4	0	2	5

Problem solving

Use the same method to answer these questions.

7 124 teams entered the Schools' Rugby Cup. Each team has 15 players. How many players were involved?

_____

8 A mobile phone package charges 19p for each minute used. How much does it cost for 689 minutes of calls?

_____

9 A word-processing program puts 372 words on each page. How many words will be on 17 pages?

_____

10 At a garden centre a machine puts 654 seeds in each packet. How many seeds will be in 18 packets?

_____

How did I find Step 5?　☐ Easy　☐ OK　☐ Difficult

Check-up test 1 Up to four-digit × one-digit, ×10, ×20, and × teen numbers

Step 1

1

		2	9	8	7
	×				5

2 $4127 \times 8 = ?$

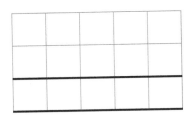

Step 2

3

		6	3	2	8
	×			1	0

4 $6789 \times 20 = ?$

Steps 3 and 4

5 $329 \times 17 = ?$

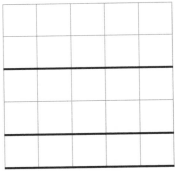

6

			1	3	8
		×		1	6
+					

Step 5

7

			7	3	4
		×		1	5
+					

8

			8	8	8
		×		1	9
+					

Steps 1 to 5 mixed

Use the grid below for working.

9 Tins of beans weigh 443g each. How heavy are
12 tins of beans?   _____   ☐ 9

10 A moped travels 13km for every litre of petrol.
How far can it travel using 165 litres?   _____   ☐ 10

11 An author writes 14 pages every day.
How many pages does she write in 731 days?   _____   ☐ 11

12 A firm makes ladders. Each ladder has 16 rungs.
How many rungs are needed to make 281 ladders?   _____   ☐ 12

Total test score

Score	1	2	3	4	5	6	7	8	9	10	11	12
%	8	17	25	33	42	50	58	67	75	83	92	100

☐ 12

Step 6: Three-digit × any two-digit multiple of 10

In Step 2 you practised multiplying by 10 or 20. Multiplying by 30, 40, 50 or any other two-digit multiple of 10 is just as easy!

$746 \times 40 = ?$

What to do (a reminder)

1 As you are multiplying by a multiple of 10, first write zero in the units column.

TTh	Th	H	T	U
		7	4	6
×			4	0
			4	0
			2	

2 Then multiply the three-digit number by the other digit of the multiple of 10, which is 4 here. Write the digits of the answer one place to the left. Start with the units as before: $6 \times 4 = 24$. Carry 2 across and write the 4.

3 Now multiply the tens digit and add the carried digit.

4 Then multiply the hundreds digit, add the carried digit and complete your answer.

		7	4	6
×			4	0
2	9	8	4	0
2	1	2		

Now you try

1

		3	7	8
×			4	0
			2	0
		3		

2

		8	2	5
×			9	0
			5	0
		4		

3

		9	6	7
×			3	0
			1	0
		2		

4

		6	8	4
×			8	0
				0

More practice

5

		6	3	2
×			6	0

6

		7	6	1
×			7	0

Set out these questions yourself to answer them.

7 469 × 80 = ?

TTh	Th	H	T	U

8 667 × 90 = ?

TTh	Th	H	T	U

Problem solving

Circle 'true' or 'false' for each question.

9 564 × 30 has the same answer as 423 × 40.

true / false

10 363 × 80 has the same answer as 967 × 30.

true / false

11 456 × 90 has the same answer as 684 × 60.

true / false

12 448 × 70 has an answer that is 400 more than 516 × 60.

true / false

How did I find Step 6?   ☐ Easy   ☐ OK   ☐ Difficult

Step 7: Two- and three-digit × two-digit no carrying in the addition

H	T	U
	1	1	4
×		3	4

When multiplying by a two-digit number you multiply by the unit digit and the multiple of 10 separately. So, to multiply by 34, you multiply by 4 and then by 30 and then add the answers.

What to do

$114 \times 34 = ?$

1. In the first row under the question multiply the top number by the units digit of the bottom number: 114×4. Remember to work from right to left and to carry if necessary.

	Th	H	T	U
		1	1	4
×			3	4
		4	5₁	6	← 114×4

2. In the next row multiply the top number by the multiple of 10. To multiply by 30, simply write a zero in the units column first and then multiply the top number by 3, carrying if necessary. $114 \times 30 = 3420$

3. Finally add your two answers. Be careful not to add the carry marks you used when multiplying. Just add the digits of the two answers. $456 + 3420 = 3876$

	Th	H	T	U
		1	1	4
×			3	4
		4	5₁	6
+	3	4₁	2	0	← 114×30
	3	8	7	6

Now you try

1

			7	2
×			6	3
		2₂	1	6	← 72×3
+				0	← 72×60

2

			7	1
×			5	6
		₄	2	6	← 71×6
+					← 71×50

3

		1	1	6
×			2	3
		3	4₁	8	← 116×3
+					← 116×20

4

		2	8	1
×			3	5
		₄	0	5	← 281×5
+					← 281×30

More practice

5

		1	0	6
	×		6	6
					← 106 × 6
+					← 106 × 60

6

		2	3	4
	×		3	8
					← 234 × 8
+					← 234 × 30

7

			6	7
	×		3	9
					← 67 × 9
+					← 67 × 30

8

		1	0	4
	×		5	7
					← 104 × 7
+					← 104 × 50

et out these questions yourself to answer them.

9 71 × 66 = ?

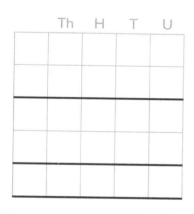

10 203 × 43 = ?

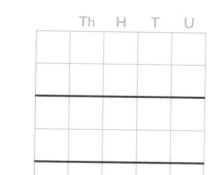

Problem solving

1 If there are 52 weeks in every year,
how many weeks are there in 28 years?

How did I find Step 7? ☐ Easy ☐ OK ☐ Difficult

Step 8: Two- and three-digit × two-digit with carrying in the addition

These are similar but, when you add your answers at the final stage, you might need to do some carrying.

What to do

$251 \times 36 = ?$

1 First multiply the top number by the units digit of the bottom number: 251×6. Remember to work from right to left and to carry if necessary.

2 In the next row multiply the top number by 30. Simply write a zero in the units column first and then multiply the top number by 3. $251 \times 30 = 7530$

3 Finally add your two answers. Be careful not to add the carry marks you used when multiplying. Just add the digits of the two answers. But you might need to carry when adding. Here 5 hundreds + 5 hundreds = 10 hundreds so we carry 1 thousand. $1506 + 7530 = 9036$

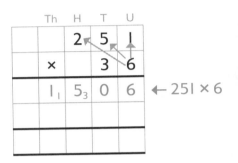

Now you try

1

		1	8	6
	×		4	4
			₂4	0	← 186 × 4
+				0	← 186 × 40

2

			9	4
		×	5	7
			₂8		← 94 × 7
+				0	← 94 × 50

3

		2	7	3
	×		3	6
			₁8		← 273 × 6
+				0	← 273 × 30

4

		1	3	8
		×	6	9
			₇2		← 138 × 9
+					← 138 × 60

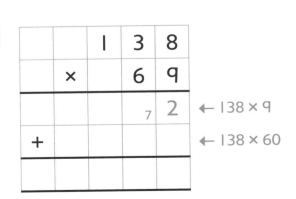

More practice

5

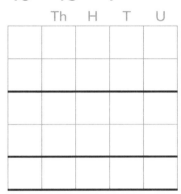

		1	2	6
	×		7	6
					← 126 × 6
+					← 126 × 70

6

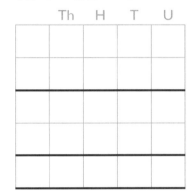

		1	8	7
	×		2	8
					← 187 × 8
+					← 187 × 10

Set out these questions yourself to answer them.

7   96 × 43 = ?

Th	H	T	U

8   159 × 53 = ?

Th	H	T	U

Problem solving

1   Answer each of these multiplications using this method.

11 × 99 = _____

22 × 99 = _____

33 × 99 = _____

Then look for patterns in the digits of the answers.
Can you use what you notice to predict the answer of 99 × 99?   _____

How did I find Step 8?   ☐ Easy   ☐ OK   ☐ Difficult

Step 9: Three-digit × two-digit five-digit answers

Do these in the same way. Some of your answers may be five-digit numbers.

What to do

$984 \times 73 = ?$

1 First multiply the top number by the units digit of the bottom number. $984 \times 3 = 2952$

TTh	Th	H	T	U	
		9	8	4	
	×		7	3	
		2_2	9_2	5_1	2	← 984 × 3
+					

2 In the next row multiply the top number by 70. $984 \times 70 = 68880$

3 Finally add your two answers. Be careful not to add the carry marks you used when multiplying. Just add the digits of the two answers. You might need to carry when adding. $2952 + 68880 = 71832$

		9	8	4	
	×		7	3	
		2_2	9_2	5_1	2	
+	6_6	8_5	8_2	8	0	← 984 × 70
	7	1	8	3	2

Now you try

1

			7	4	2	
		×		6	6	
				$_1$	2	← 742 × 6
+					0	← 742 × 60

2

			3	6	5	
		×		8	9	
				$_4$	5	← 365 × 9
+					0	← 365 × 80

3

			8	7	3	
		×		3	4	
				$_1$	2	← 873 × 4
+					0	← 873 × 30

4

			9	5	8	
		×		7	8	
				$_6$	4	← 958 × 8
+						← 958 × 7

More practice

Each of these questions has a missing digit. Can you work out which digit is missing in each?

5

			5	7	6
	×		◯		6
		3₃	4₄	5₃	6
+	2₂	3₃	0₂	4	**0**
	2	6	4	9	6

6

			◯	1	7
		×		8	9
		6₆	4₁	5₆	3
+	5₅	7₁	3₅	6	**0**
	6	3	8	1	3

Problem solving

7 Each box of pins contains 234 pins.
How many pins will be in 76 boxes?

_____

8 What is 333 × 33?

_____

 Which is larger: 578 × 46 or 678 × 39?

_____

Step 10: Four- and five-digit × two-digit

Now you can try to multiply larger numbers by two-digit numbers.

$12\,504 \times 53 = ?$

What to do

1 First multiply the top number by the units digit of the bottom number, working from right to left as always. $12\,504 \times 3 = 37\,512$

	HTh	TTh	Th	H	T	U
			1	2	5	0	4
×					5	3
		3	7₁	5	1₁	2	← $12\,504 \times 3$
+						

2 In the next row multiply the top number by 50. $12\,504 \times 50 = 625\,200$

3 Finally add your two answers. Be careful not to add the carry marks you used when multiplying. Just add the digits of the two answers. You might need to carry when adding. $37\,512 + 625\,200 = 662\,712$

			1	2	5	0	4
×					5	3
			3	7₁	5	1₁	2
+	6₁	2₂	5	2₂	0	0	← $12\,504 \times 50$
	6	6	2	7	1	2

Now you try

1

			3	1	4	6
×					2	4
					₂4		← 3146 × 4
+						0	← 3146 × 20

2

			7	2	8	3
×					7	5
					₁5	← 7283 × 5
+					0	← 7283 × 7

3

		1	1	1	1	1
×					3	6
					6	← 11111 × 6
+					0	← 11111 × 30

4

		1	5	1	8	9
×					6	2
					₁8	← 15189 ×
+					0	← 15189 ×

More practice   Set out these questions yourself to answer them.

5 1546 × 88 = ?

HTh	TTh	Th	H	T	U

6 12 463 × 33 = ?

HTh	TTh	Th	H	T	U

Problem solving

7 Each letter stands for a digit in this multiplication.

Choose a digit to stand for the letter A, for example
2222 × 22 or 5555 × 55.

Find the answer and see
if it matches the solution
shown.

If not, using spare paper,
try again with different digits.

Can you work out which
digit the letter A stands
for here?

			A	A	A	A
	×				A	A
		C	A	A	A	B
+	C	A	A	A	B	D
	A	C	A	A	D	B

A = _____

8 Peter earns £18 423 each year. How many years will it take him to earn over one million
pounds? Will it take him 33 years, 55 years or 77 years?

_____

How did I find Step 10?   ☐ Easy   ☐ OK   ☐ Difficult

Check-up test 2 Up to five-digit × two-digit

Step 6

1

		6	8	9
×			3	0

2 412 × 80 = ?

Steps 7 and 8

3

		1	2	4
×			6	2
					← 124 × 2
+					← 124 × 60

4 68 × 49 = ?

	×			
					← 68 × 9
+					← 68 × 40

Step 9

5

		8	9	7
×			5	7
+				

6 638 × 36 = ?

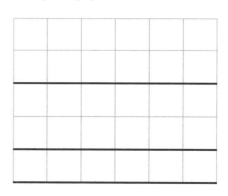

Step 10

7

		1	5	8	6	3
×					2	2
+						

8

		1	2	4	7	2
×					4	8
+						

Steps 6 to 10 mixed

Use the grid below for working.

9 Lily was paid £24 per day for one month (31 days).
How much was she paid in total?   _____   ☐ 9

10 A car travels 23km for every litre of petrol.
How far can it travel using 175 litres?   _____   ☐ 10

11 Ajay worked for 246 days. He earns £56 per day.
How much did he earn?   _____   ☐ 11

12 A bicycle factory makes 67 wheels each day.
How many wheels does it make in 365 days?   _____   ☐ 12

Total test score

Score	1	2	3	4	5	6	7	8	9	10	11	12
%	8	17	25	33	42	50	58	67	75	83	92	100

_____
12

Step 11: Three-digit × three-digit multiples of 100

You learnt in Step 6 how to multiply by a multiple of 10. Here we'll
look at multiplying by multiples of 100. They are just as easy!

H	T	U
9	7	1
× 5	0	0

What to do

$971 \times 500 = ?$

1 When multiplying by a multiple of 100, multiply first by
100. To make a number 100 times larger we move the
digits of a number two places to the left. Write two zeros
in the units and tens columns first to multiply by 100.

HTh	TTh	Th	H	T	U
			9	7	1
		×	5	0	0
				0	0

2 Then just multiply the top number by the hundreds digit of
the multiple of 100, which is 5 here. As always work from
right to left and fill in the digits two places to the left.

HTh	TTh	Th	H	T	U
			9	7	1
		×	5	0	0
4	8	5	5	0	0
4	3				

Now you try

1

			8	2	5
		×	3	0	0
			5	0	0
			1		

2

			9	6	8
		×	4	0	0
			2	0	0
		3			

3

			6	6	6
		×	9	0	0
				0	0
		5			

4

			3	4	7
		×	8	0	0
				0	0

5

			5	7	6
		×	7	0	0

6

			8	0	6
		×	6	0	0

More practice

Each of these answers has an error. Write the error that has been made and give the correct answer.

7

		8	5	3
	×	7	0	0
5	9	7	1	0
	5	3	2	

Error: _____

_____

Correct answer: _____

8

		4	4	4	
	×	9	0	0	
3	9	6	6	0	0
	3	3	3		

Error: _____

_____

Correct answer: _____

Problem solving

9 A school receives £400 per pupil to pay for equipment. If there are 128 pupils at the school, how much does it receive altogether?

_____

10 Which is larger: 562 × 300 or 256 × 700?

_____

_____

11 There is a long fence around an airport. Each fence panel is 500cm wide. If there are 852 panels around the airport, what is the total length of the fence?

_____

12 Bags of flour weigh 800g. How heavy is 467 bags of flour altogether?

_____

How did I find Step 11?   ☐ Easy   ☐ OK   ☐ Difficult

Step 12: Three-digit × three-digit multiples of 10

When multiplying numbers by three-digit multiples of 10 (such as 430 or 790), split the multiple into two parts (such as 30 and 400 or 90 and 700). Multiply the parts separately and add them.

	H	T	U
	3	8	5
×	7	9	0

What to do

$385 × 790 = ?$

1 Split the bottom number into a multiple of 10 and a multiple of 100. Think of 790 as 90 and 700. Start by multiplying the top number by 90. Simply write a zero in the units column first and multiply the top number by 9.

HTh	TTh	Th	H	T	U	
			3	8	5	
		×	7	9	0	
		3_3	4_7	6_4	5	0	← 385 × 90

2 In the second row, multiply the top number by the **hundreds** digit. So here multiply 385 by 700. Simply write two zeros in the units and tens columns and then multiply the top number by 7.

3 Finally add your two answers. Be careful **not** to add the carry marks you used when multiplying. Just add the digits of the two answers. 34 650 + 269 500 = 304 150

				3	8	5	
			×	7	9	0	
		3_3	4_7	6_4	5	0	
+	2_2	6_5	9_3	5	0	0	← 385 × 700
	3	0	4	1	5	0	

Now you try

1

			4	1	3	
		×	3	5	0	
			5	5	0	←413 × 50
+				0	0	←413 × 300

2

			4	8	7	
		×	6	6	0	
			$_4$	2	0	←487 × 6
+				0	0	←487 × 6

More practice

3

			3	4	2
		×	2	6	0
+					

4

			5	3	9
		×	7	4	0
+					

Set out these questions yourself to answer them.

5 567 × 380 = ?

HTh	TTh	Th	H	T	U

6 914 × 870 = ?

HTh	TTh	Th	H	T	U

Problem solving

7 A rectangular carpet has a length of 153cm and a width of 250cm. What is its area?

_____

8 ☐ ÷ 420 = 129

Write in the missing number.

Step 13: Multiplying two three-digit numbers
easier tables facts

Now you should be feeling confident to put it all together and multiply three-digit numbers. Simply split the bottom number into a one-digit number, a multiple of 10 and a multiple of 100 and multiply by each part separately.

	H	T	U
	2	5	
×	2	4	3

What to do

$251 \times 243 = ?$

1 Multiply the top number by the **units** digit of the bottom number: 251×3. Remember to work from right to left and carry if necessary.

2 In the next row multiply the top number by the **tens** digit: 251×40. Simply write a zero in the units column first and multiply the top number by 4.

3 In the third row, multiply the top number by the **hundreds** digit: 251×200. Simply write two zeros in the units and tens columns and then multiply the top number by 2.

4 Finally add your three answers.

	TTh	Th	H	T	U	
			2	5	1	
×			2	4	3	
			7₁	5	3	← 251 × 3
	1₁	0₂	0	4	0	← 251 × 40
+	5₁	0	2	0	0	← 251 × 200
	6	0	9	9	3	

Now you try

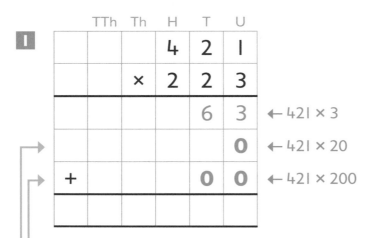

1

	TTh	Th	H	T	U	
			4	2	1	
×			2	2	3	
				6	3	← 421 × 3
					0	← 421 × 20
+				0	0	← 421 × 200

2

	TTh	Th	H	T	U	
			2	5	3	
×			1	4	4	
						← 253 ×
					0	← 253 ×
+				0	0	← 253 ×

What have 421×20 and 421×200 got in common?

More practice

3

			3	2	1
		×	1	3	5
+					

4

			4	2	4
		×	3	3	3
+					

Set out these questions yourself to answer them.

5 543 × 245 = ?

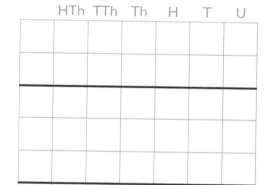

6 542 × 355 = ?

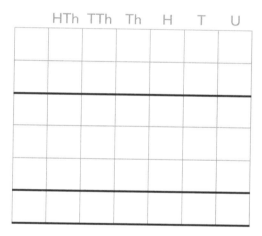

Problem solving

7 Find the answer to 331 × 214.

_____

8 A factory makes 621 TVs every day. How many TVs are made in 365 days?

_____

How did I find Step 13?   ☐ Easy   ☐ OK   ☐ Difficult

Step 14: Multiplying two three-digit numbers
harder tables facts

These questions include harder tables facts but are done in the same way as in Step 13. Some people start with the multiple of 100. The order you multiply each part does not matter, as the final answer will be the same when you add the parts.

What to do

$879 \times 676 = ?$

1 Remember to multiply each part separately, adding zeros and carrying as necessary.

2 Add your three answers. Be careful not to add the carry marks you used when multiplying.

HTh	TTh	Th	H	T	U	
			8	7	9	
		×	6	7	6	
		5_5	2_4	7_5	4	← 879×6
	6_6	1_5	5_6	3	0	← 879×70
+	5_5	2_4	7_5	4	0	0	← 879×600
	5	9	4	2	0	4

Now you try

1

			9	9	6
		×	5	7	3
			2	8_1	8
					0
+				0	0

2

			6	7	6
		×	1	8	8
				$_4$	8
					0
+				0	0

3

			8	4	7
		×	6	6	9
				2_6	3
					0
+				0	0

4

			4	9	6
		×	7	2	7
					0
+				0	0

More practice

Set out these questions yourself to answer them.

5 687 × 395 = ?

HTh	TTh	Th	H	T	U

6 617 × 577 = ?

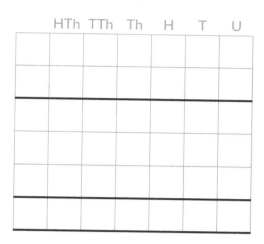

Problem solving

7 Find the missing number in this division: [   ] ÷ 345 = 789
Also write the answer in words.

_____

_____

8 A farmer has a field with a length of 653m and a width of 478m. What is the area of the field?

_____

How did I find Step 14? ☐ Easy ☐ OK ☐ Difficult

Check-up test 3 Three-digit × three-digit

Step 11

1

			6	8	4
		×	3	0	0

2 458 × 800 = ?

Step 12

3

			4	6	6
		×	8	3	0

4 917 × 570 = ?

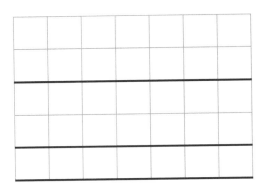

Steps 13 and 14

5

			4	2	6
		×	3	3	3

6 687 × 862 = ?

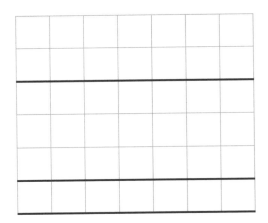

Steps 11 to 14 mixed

Use the grid below for working.

7 There are 586 pupils in a school. Each raises £180 for charity. How much is raised in total?

_____   ☐ 7

8 A concert venue sells 450 tickets per performance. If there are 246 performances in a year and all the tickets are sold, how many tickets are sold in total?

_____   ☐ 8

9 A fishing boat is allowed to catch 476kg of fish per day. How many kilograms of fish is it allowed to catch each year (365 days)?

_____   ☐ 9

10 On a mobile phone network 412 mobiles made 306 minutes of calls each. How many minutes in total is this?

_____   ☐ 10

Total test score

Score	1	2	3	4	5	6	7	8	9	10
%	10	20	30	40	50	60	70	80	90	100

☐
___
10

Step 15: Simple decimals × one-digit

Now that you can multiply whole numbers, multiplying decimals is almost as easy! All you need to do is to remember how many times smaller a decimal is than its related whole number.

$6.8 ×$

What to do

$6.8 × 3 = ?$

1 Write the multiplication question as a new question **without** a decimal point.

$68 × 3 = ?$

2 Answer the new whole number question. $68 × 3 = 204$

	H	T	U
		6	8
×			3
	2	0	4
	2	2	

3 Decide how many times smaller the decimal question is than the new whole number question. Here 6.8 is ten times smaller than 68. So the answer to the decimal question will be ten times smaller than the whole number question.

4 Finally adjust the answer so that it matches the original question. To divide a number by 10, move the digits one place to the right. To divide by 100, move the digits two places to the right.

$6.8 × 3$ is ten times smaller than $68 × 3$, so $6.8 × 3 = 20.4$

Now you try

1 $4.7 × 3 = ?$

		4	7
×			3
			1
		2	

$4.7 × 3$ is ☐ times smaller than $47 × 3$,

so $4.7 × 3 =$ ☐

2 $0.35 × 5 = ?$

		3	5
×			5
			5
		2	

$0.35 × 5$ is 100 times smaller than $35 × 5$,

so $0.35 × 5 =$ ☐

3 $43 × 0.4 = ?$

		4	3
×			4
			2
		1	

$43 × 0.4$ is ☐ times smaller than $43 × 4$,

so $43 × 0.4 =$ ☐

More practice

Set out these questions yourself to answer them.

4 0.36 × 6 = ?

.36 × 6 is [   ] times

maller than 36 × 6,

0.36 × 6 = [   ]

5 9.7 × 7 = ?

9.7 × 7 is [   ] times

smaller than 97 × 7,

so 9.7 × 7 = [   ]

6 29 × 0.8 = ?

29 × 0.8 is [   ] times

smaller than 29 × 8,

so 29 × 0.8 = [   ]

Problem solving

A bottle can hold 0.7 litres of water. How many litres would 18 of these bottles hold?

A car travels 9.3km on a litre of petrol. How far will it travel on 8 litres of petrol?

It takes a printer 6.7 seconds to print a photo. How many seconds will it take to print five of these photos?

Each fence panel is 0.89 metres long. How long are eight of these panels altogether?

How did I find Step 15? ☐ Easy ☐ OK ☐ Difficult

Step 16: Simple decimals × two-digit

In the same way, you can now multiply decimals using long multiplication. 7.4×34

What to do

$7.4 \times 34 = ?$

1 Write the multiplication question as a new question without a decimal point.

$74 \times 34 = ?$

2 Use the written method to answer the new whole number question. $74 \times 34 = 2516$

Th	H	T	U	
		7	4	
×		3	4	
	2_2	9_1	6	← 74 × 4
+ 2_2	2_1	2	0	← 74 × 30
2	5	1	6	← 296 + 2220

3 Decide how many times smaller the decimal question is than the new whole number question. Here 7.4 is ten times smaller than 74, so the answer to the decimal question will be ten times smaller than the whole number question.

4 Finally adjust the answer so that it matches the original question. Here make 2516 ten times smaller than the whole number question.
$2516 \div 10 = 251.6$

7.4×34 is ten times smaller than 74×34, so $7.4 \times 34 = 251.6$

Now you try

1 $4.5 \times 38 = ?$

		4	5
×		3	8
		$_4$	0
+			0

4.5 × 38 is ☐ times smaller than

45 × 38, so 4.5 × 38 = ☐

2 $0.81 \times 56 = ?$

		8	1
×		5	6
			6
+			

0.81 × 56 is ☐ times smaller than

81 × 56, so 0.81 × 56 = ☐

More practice

et out these questions yourself to answer them.

3 7.2 × 63 = ?

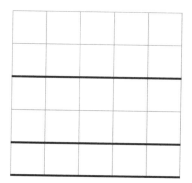

.2 × 63 is ☐ times smaller than

2 × 63, so 7.2 × 63 = ☐

4 27 × 8.4 = ?

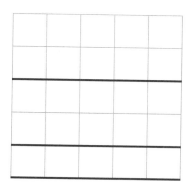

27 × 8.4 is ☐ times smaller than

27 × 84, so 27 × 8.4 = ☐

Problem solving

5 71 × 6.6 = ?

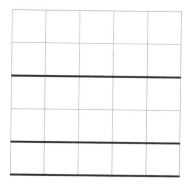

× 6.6 is ☐ times smaller than

× 66, so 71 × 6.6 = ☐

6 2.03 × 43 = ?

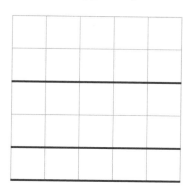

2.03 × 43 is ☐ times smaller than

203 × 43, so 2.03 × 43 = ☐

How did I find Step 16?   ☐ Easy   ☐ OK   ☐ Difficult

Step 17: Multiplying two decimals with one decimal place

When multiplying two decimals together, adjust the answer in the same way. For example, 5.1×3.6 is 100 times smaller than 51×36. So you find the answer to 51×36 and then divide by 100.

5.1×3.6

What to do

1 Write the question without the decimal points.

2 Answer the new whole number question.

3 Decide how many times smaller the original question is and adjust the answer.

4 A useful way to check if you have put the decimal point in the correct place is to count up the number of digits after the decimal points in the question and then check that the same number of digits are after the decimal point in the answer: $5.\underline{1} \times 3.\underline{6} = 18.\underline{36}$

$5.1 \times 3.6 = ?$

$51 \times 36 = ?$

	Th	H	T	U
			5	1
×			3	6
		3_3	0	6
+	1_1	5	3	**0**
	1	8	3	6

5.1×3.6 is 100 times smaller than 51×36, so $5.1 \times 3.6 = 18.36$

Now you try

1 $2.5 \times 5.6 = ?$

			2	5
×			5	6
			$_3$	0
+				0

2.5×5.6 is ☐ times smaller than 25×56, so $2.5 \times 5.6 =$ ☐

2 $3.2 \times 9.8 = ?$

			3	2
×			9	8
			$_1$	6
+				

3.2×9.8 is ☐ times smaller than 32×98, so $3.2 \times 9.8 =$ ☐

More practice

et out these questions yourself to answer them.

3 8.1 × 3.7 = ?

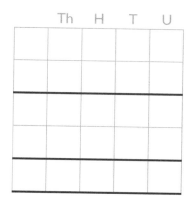

l × 3.7 is ⬚ times smaller than

l × 37, so 8.1 × 3.7 = ⬚

4 7.6 × 4.3 = ?

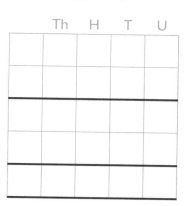

7.6 × 4.3 is ⬚ times smaller than

76 × 43, so 7.6 × 4.3 = ⬚

Problem solving

Find the product of
6.3 and 3.9.

_____

A rug has a length of
4.3m and a width of 2.8m.
What is the area of the rug?

_____

How did I find Step 17?   ☐ Easy   ☐ OK   ☐ Difficult

Step 18: **Multiplying two decimals** with one or two decimal places

Well done – you are at the last step! These questions are similar to the last few steps, but sometimes may involve numbers that are 1000 times smaller than the whole number questions, for example 9.84×7.3 is 1000 times smaller than 984×73.

$9.84 \times 7.$

What to do

$9.84 \times 7.3 = ?$

1 Write the question without the decimal points.

$984 \times 73 = ?$

2 Answer the whole number question.

3 Decide how many times smaller the original question is and adjust the answer.

4 Count up the number of digits after the decimal points in the question and check that the answer has the same number: $9.\underline{84} \times 7.\underline{3} = 71.\underline{832}$

	TTh	Th	H	T	U
			9	8	4
		×		7	3
			2_2	9_2	5_1	2
+	6_6	8_5	8_2	8	0
	7	1	8	3	2

9.84×7.3 is 1000 times smaller than 984×73, so $9.84 \times 7.3 = 71.832$

Now you try

1 $1.24 \times 5.6 = ?$

		1	2	4
	×		5	6
			$_2$	4
+				0

1.24×5.6 is [ ] times smaller than 124×56, so $1.24 \times 5.6 =$ [ ]

2 $3.35 \times 9.8 = ?$

		3	3	5
			9	8
			$_4$	0

3.35×9.8 is [ ] times smaller than 335×98, so $3.35 \times 9.8 =$ [ ]

More practice

Write the missing decimal in each question using these whole number calculations to help.

			5	7	6
		×		4	6
		3_3	4_4	5_3	6
+	2_2	3_3	0_2	4	**0**
	2	6	4	9	6

			7	1	7
		×		8	9
		6_6	4_1	5_6	3
+	5_5	7_1	3_5	6	**0**
	6	3	8	1	3

1 5.76 × [   ] = 26.496

2 57.6 × [   ] = 264.96

3 576 × [   ] = 2649.6

4 [   ] × 8.9 = 63.813

6 [   ] × 8.9 = 638.13

8 [   ] × 89 = 6381.3

Problem solving

Which is larger: 57.8 × 4.6 or 6.78 × 3.9?

_____

_____

10 What is 3.33 × 3.3?

_____

11 What is 6.66 × 6.6?

_____

How did I find Step 18?   ☐ Easy   ☐ OK   ☐ Difficult

Final test Long multiplication of whole numbers and decimals

Steps 15 to 18

1 $2.7 \times 6 = ?$

		2	7
×			6

2.7×6 is [＿＿] times

smaller than 27×6,

so $2.7 \times 6 =$ [＿＿]

2 $0.38 \times 5 = ?$

		3	8
×			5

0.38×5 is [＿＿] times

smaller than 38×5,

so $0.38 \times 5 =$ [＿＿]

3 $27 \times 2.6 = ?$

		2	7
×		2	6
+			

27×2.6 is [＿＿] times

smaller than 27×26,

so $27 \times 2.6 =$ [＿＿]

4 $8.35 \times 6.1 = ?$

		8	3	5
			6	1

8.35×6.1 is [＿＿] times

smaller than 835×61,

so $8.35 \times 6.1 =$ [＿＿]

Steps 1 to 18 mixed

Use spare paper for working.

Find the product of 5137 and 20.

_____ ☐ 5

A cinema has 66 seats in each row. If there are
38 rows, how many seats are there in total?

_____ ☐ 6

There are 16 biscuits in each pack.
How many biscuits are there in 86 packs?

_____ ☐ 7

Chloe runs on 143 days. If each run is 13km,
how far does she run in total?

_____ ☐ 8

How many hours are there in 365 days?

_____ ☐ 9

What is 444 × 44?

_____ ☐ 10

A plane travels an average of 756km each day
for 230 days a year. How many kilometres is this?

_____ ☐ 11

A farmer has a field with a length of 654m and
a width of 448m. What is the area of the field?

_____ ☐ 12

Find the product of 3.62 and 3.1.

_____ ☐ 13

A shop sold 37 computers in one month.
Each computer sold for £389. How much
did the shop get for them?

_____ ☐ 14

What is 637 × 588?

_____ ☐ 15

What is 5.55 × 5.5?

_____ ☐ 16

Total test score ☐

Score	1	2	3	4	5	6	7	8	9	10	11	12	13	14	15	16
%	6	13	19	25	31	38	44	50	56	63	69	75	81	88	94	100

16

Schofield&Sims

the long-established educational publisher specialising in maths, English and science

Written Calculation comprises six **Pupil Books**, six **Answer Books**, a **Teacher's Guide** and a **Teacher's Resource Book** and uses methods recommended in the National Curriculum. Designed for use at Key Stage 2, each **Pupil Book** uses 18 carefully structured steps to guide the learner towards full mastery of each written method, supporting them in their national tests and other areas of the National Curriculum. **Written Calculation** also helps pupils develop confidence and fluency in their learning by practising and embedding place value, number facts and problem solving skills. The importance of estimating and checking answers is also emphasised.

Written Calculation: Multiplication 2 leads pupils from short multiplication to long multiplication. Pupils beginning this book should have completed **Multiplication 1**. Pupils should have an understanding of the value of digits up to and beyond four-digit numbers and experience of multiplying single-digit numbers together. Pupils who have learnt their times tables will find written multiplication easier.

Each of the 18 steps features the following sections.
- *What to do* – detailed explanations and a worked example.
- *Now you try* – questions that are similar to those in the worked example.
- *More practice* – questions that are more difficult and provide less support than those in *Now you try*.
- *Problem solving* – word problems.
- *Self-evaluation rating* – to help identify pupils who may be struggling with the step.

Three *Check-up tests* and a *Final test* enable you to monitor pupils' progress and quickly convert scores to percentages. These scores may later be recorded on the *Group record sheet*.

The accompanying **Teacher's Guide** provides useful notes and ideas for planning lessons, enabling a whole-school approach. Detailed *Teaching notes* outline clear learning objectives and a *Summary of the steps* for each **Pupil Book** is included. Photocopiable *Assessment resources* allow you to monitor and assess pupils' progress.

Supplementary *Further practice* and *Problem solving questions* can be found in the **Teacher's Resource Book**. These photocopiable resources may be used for further practice, assessment, revision or homework and correspond to the steps covered in each of the **Pupil Books**.

The full range of books in the series is as follows.

Addition	978 0 7217 1266 6	**Addition Answers**	978 0 7217 1272 7
Subtraction	978 0 7217 1267 3	**Subtraction Answers**	978 0 7217 1273 4
Multiplication 1	978 0 7217 1268 0	**Multiplication 1 Answers**	978 0 7217 1274 1
Multiplication 2	978 0 7217 1269 7	**Multiplication 2 Answers**	978 0 7217 1275 8
Division 1	978 0 7217 1270 3	**Division 1 Answers**	978 0 7217 1276 5
Division 2	978 0 7217 1271 0	**Division 2 Answers**	978 0 7217 1277 2
Teacher's Guide	978 0 7217 1278 9	**Teacher's Resource Book**	978 0 7217 1300 7

Free downloads, available from the **Written Calculation** page of the Schofield & Sims website, enhance the effectiveness of the series. These are updated as necessary to ensure that **Schofield & Sims Written Calculation** meets the requirements of the National Curriculum.

ISBN 978-07217-1269-7

9 780721 712697

ISBN 978 0 7217 1269 7
Key Stage 2
Age range from 7 years
£3.50
(Retail price)

For further information and to place your order visit
www.schofieldandsims.co.uk or telephone 01484 607080